CW00349271

Make it easy...
Maths
Quick Tests

Age 10-11

Paul Broadbent and Peter Patilla

Test 1 Multiply and divide by 10, 100 and 1000

When **multiplying by 10, 100** or **1000** move the digits the correct number of places **to the left**.

When **dividing by 10, 100** or **1000** move the digits the correct number of places **to the right**.

Write the missing numbers.

1. 36 × ⬚ = 36000

2. 4.21 × 100 = ⬚

3. ⬚ ÷ 10 = 78.5

4. 0.9 × ⬚ = 9

5. 1603 ÷ 100 = ⬚

6. ⬚ ÷ 100 = 451

7. 1000 × ⬚ = 6338000

8. 9720 ÷ ⬚ = 97.2

9. 340 ÷ 1000 = ⬚

10. ⬚ × 100 = 201

Colour in your score

Test 1

Test 2 Division facts

Use **multiplication facts** to help work out **division facts**.

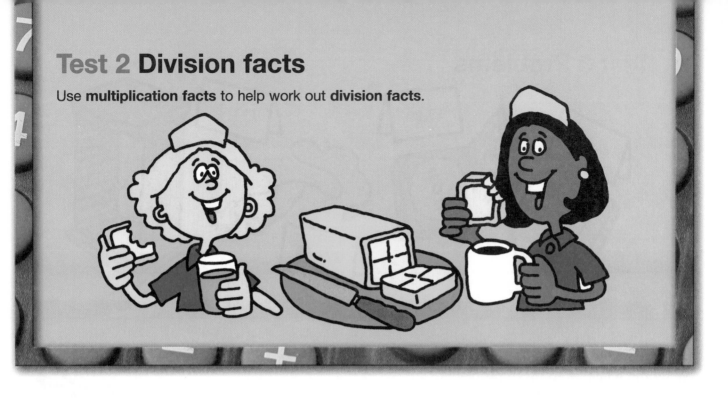

Answer these.

1. 81 ÷ 9 =
2. 56 ÷ 7 =
3. 28 ÷ 4 =
4. 42 ÷ 6 =
5. 27 ÷ 3 =
6. 24 ÷ 8 =
7. 35 ÷ 7 =
8. 54 ÷ 9 =
9. 32 ÷ 8 =
10. 48 ÷ 6 =

Colour in your score

Test 2

Test 3 Problems

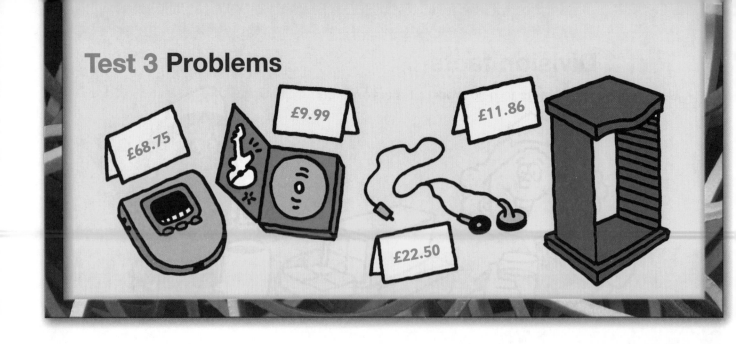

£68.75   £9.99   £11.86   £22.50

Write the answers to these problems.

1. What is the cost of 4 CD's?

2. How much change would there be from £100 if you bought the CD player?

3. What is the difference in price between the CD holder and the headphones?

4. What is the total cost of the CD player, the headphones and the CD holder?

5. How much change would there be from £50 if you bought 3 CD's?

6. 42cm is cut off a length of wood 4.5m long. The rest is cut into 6 equal lengths. What is the length of each piece?

7. If a glass holds 280ml and 4 glasses are filled from a 2 litre bottle full of milk, how much milk is left?

8. Cinema tickets for an adult cost £4.35 and £2.96 for a child. A family ticket for 2 adults and 2 children costs £12.00. How much is saved by buying a family ticket?

9. David is 33cm taller than his sister. She is half the height of their father, who is 178cm tall. How tall is David?

10. 3 parcels weigh a total of 2kg. 2 of the parcels weigh the same amount and the other is half the weight of one of the other parcels. What is the weight of each parcel?

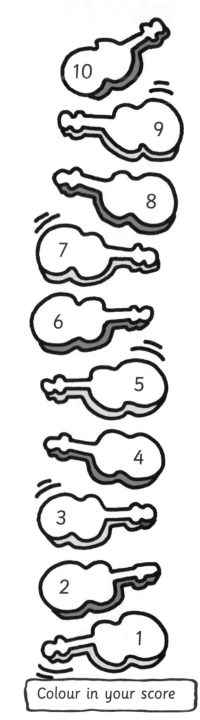

Colour in your score

Test 3

Test 4 Fractions

To **order fractions**, change them so they all have the **same denominator**.

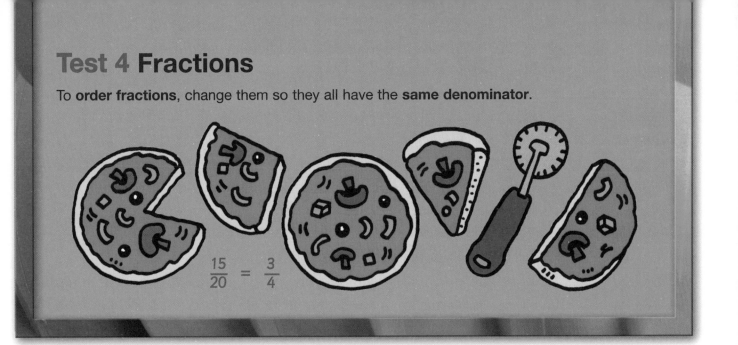

$$\frac{15}{20} = \frac{3}{4}$$

Simplify these fractions.

1. $\frac{20}{25}$ = ☐

2. $\frac{14}{21}$ = ☐

3. $\frac{18}{24}$ = ☐

4. $\frac{9}{15}$ = ☐

5. $\frac{20}{24}$ = ☐

Write these fractions in order starting with the smallest.

6. $\frac{1}{2}$ $\frac{5}{6}$ $\frac{3}{4}$ $\frac{7}{8}$ ☐ ☐ ☐ ☐

7. $\frac{10}{20}$ $\frac{6}{20}$ $\frac{14}{20}$ $\frac{15}{20}$ ☐ ☐ ☐ ☐

8. $\frac{3}{6}$ $\frac{12}{18}$ $\frac{5}{6}$ $\frac{4}{18}$ ☐ ☐ ☐ ☐

9. $\frac{15}{20}$ $\frac{4}{20}$ $\frac{10}{20}$ $\frac{6}{20}$ ☐ ☐ ☐ ☐

10. $\frac{25}{40}$ $\frac{20}{40}$ $\frac{10}{40}$ $\frac{16}{40}$ ☐ ☐ ☐ ☐

10
9
8
7
6
5
4
3
2
1

Colour in your score

Test 4

Test 5 Ratio and proportion

Ratio is used to **compare 2 quantities.**

Proportion is the **fraction of the whole.**

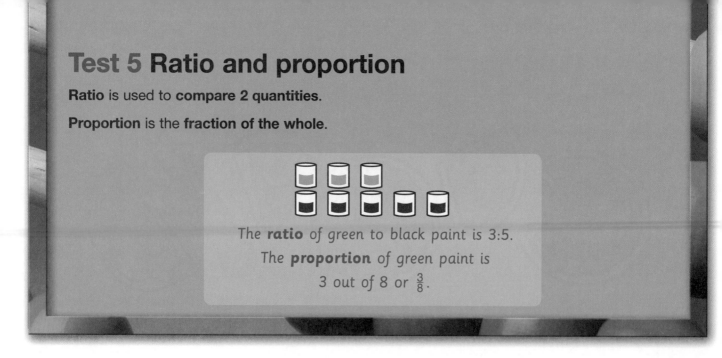

The **ratio** of green to black paint is 3:5.
The **proportion** of green paint is
3 out of 8 or $\frac{3}{8}$.

Write the ratios of green paint to black paint.

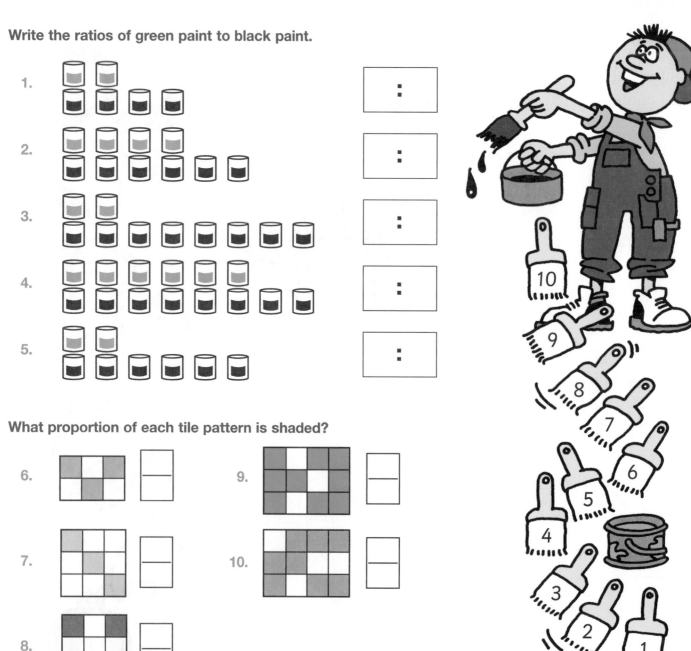

1.

:

2.

:

3.

:

4.

:

5.

:

What proportion of each tile pattern is shaded?

6.

7.

8.

9.

10.

Colour in your score

Test 5

Test 6 Averages

Mean, mode and **median** are all different types of **averages**.

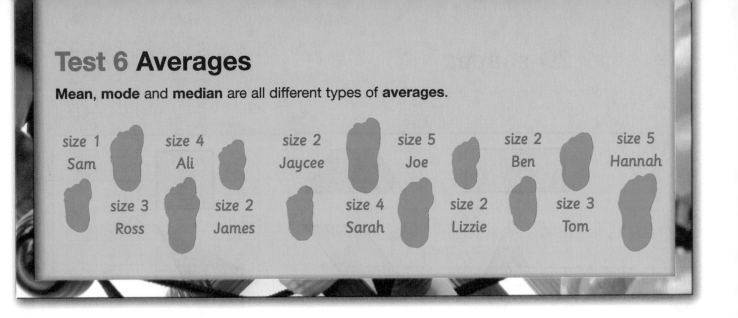

size 1 Sam   size 4 Ali   size 2 Jaycee   size 5 Joe   size 2 Ben   size 5 Hannah

size 3 Ross   size 2 James   size 4 Sarah   size 2 Lizzie   size 3 Tom

Write the answers to these problems.

1. Write the shoe sizes in order starting with the smallest.

2. What is the mean size of all the children?

3. What is the median size?

4. What is the mode size?

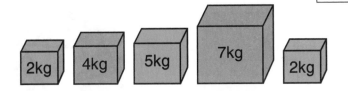

2kg   4kg   5kg   7kg   2kg

5. What is the median weight of the boxes?

6. What is the mode weight?

7. What is the mean weight of all the boxes?

34   29   27   32   27   34   27

8. What is the mean of these numbers?

9. What is the mode?

10. What is the median?

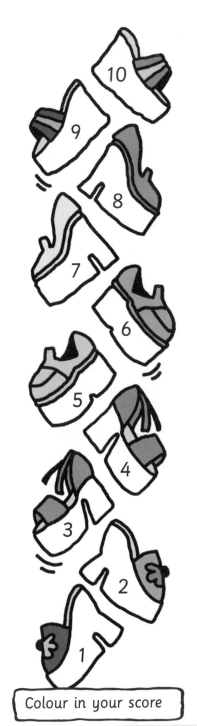

Colour in your score

Test 6

Test 7 2D shapes

It is important to know the names of **2D shapes**.

A B C

D E F

Write the answers to these questions.

1. Which shape is a parallelogram?

2. What is the name of shape A?

3. Which shape is a square?

4. What is the name of shape F?

5. Which shape is a rhombus?

6. What is the name of shape B?

7. What are all of these shapes called?

8. Which shape has 4 right angles and 4 equal sides?

Draw lines of symmetry on each shape.

9.

10.

10
9
8
7
6
5
4
3
2
1

Colour in your score

Test 7

Test 8 Measures

Pints and gallons are imperial units of measure; litres are metric units of measure. These graphs convert between different units.

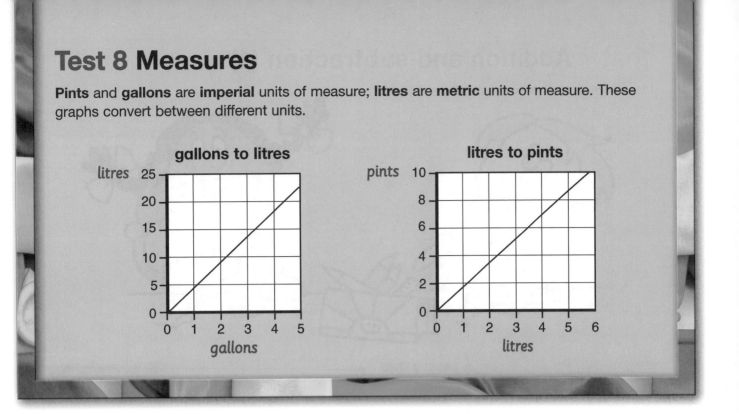

gallons to litres

litres 25 –
20 –
15 –
10 –
5 –
0 –
0 1 2 3 4 5
gallons

litres to pints

pints 10 –
8 –
6 –
4 –
2 –
0 –
0 1 2 3 4 5 6
litres

Use the conversion graphs above to write the missing measures.

(≈ means approximately equal to.)

1. ☐ litres ≈ 2 gallons

2. 7 pints ≈ ☐ litres

3. ☐ pints ≈ 1.2 litres

4. ☐ gallons ≈ 22.5 litres

5. 2 litres ≈ ☐ pints

6. ☐ litres ≈ 0.5 gallons

7. ☐ gallons ≈ 13.5 litres

8. 1.75 pints ≈ ☐ litres

9. ☐ pints ≈ 4.5 litres

10. ☐ litres ≈ 3 gallons

Colour in your score

Test 8

Test 9 Addition and subtraction (1)

Use **mental methods** to add and subtract.

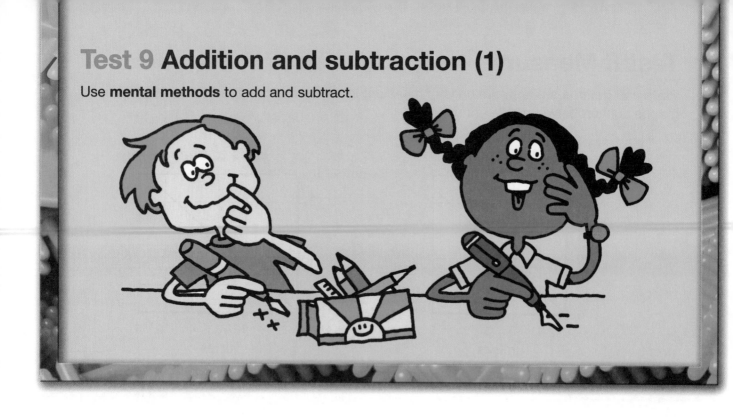

Write the answers.

1.	63	+	84	=
2.	127	–	98	=
3.	209	+	155	=
4.	4300	–	2600	=
5.	712	–	330	=
6.	960	+	450	=
7.	307	+	88	=
8.	149	–	79	=
9.	6320	–	1800	=
10.	2900	+	4700	=

Colour in your score

Test 9

Test 10 Patterns and sequences

Looking at differences between **numbers in a sequence** can show the pattern or rule.

Continue these sequences.

1. | 27 | 19 | 11 | 3 | −5 | | |

2. | −9 | 3 | 15 | 27 | 39 | | |

3. | 4.5 | 7 | 9.5 | 12 | 14.5 | | |

4. | 1 | 2 | 4 | 7 | 11 | | |

5. | 128 | 64 | 32 | 16 | 8 | | |

Write the missing numbers in these sequences.

6. | −1 | −5 | | | −17 | −21 |

7. | 1.5 | | | 2.25 | 2.5 | 2.75 |

8. | | | 37 | 43 | 49 | 55 |

9. | | 17 | | −13 | −28 | −43 |

10. | 5 | | 11 | | 25 | 35 |

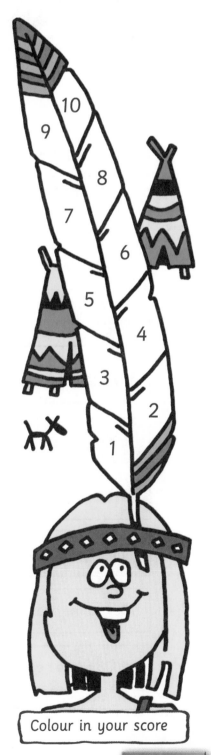

Colour in your score

Test 10

Test 11 Approximation and rounding

When you **round** to the nearest 10, 100 or 1000, the **halfway position** is important. **Halfway** points are always rounded up.

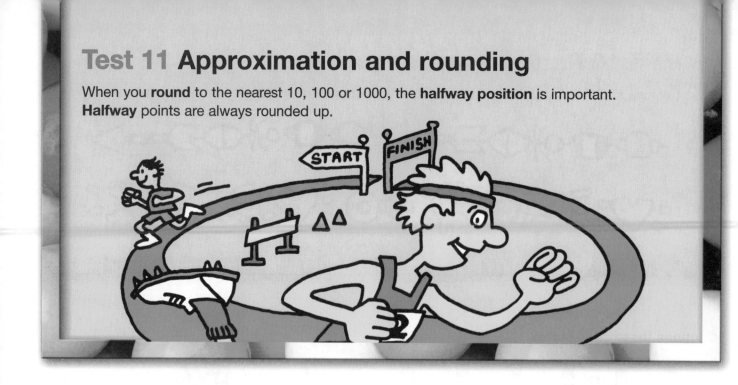

Round these numbers.

1.	35604 to the nearest 10	
2.	7955 to the nearest 100	
3.	81428 to the nearest 1000	
4.	2365 to the nearest 10	
5.	177912 to the nearest 1000	
6.	900648 to the nearest 100	
7.	39524 to the nearest 1000	
8.	11870 to the nearest 100	
9.	7651 to the nearest 10	
10.	22098 to the nearest 1000	

Colour in your score

Test 11

Test 12 Multiplying decimals

Estimate first to check an answer.

Answer these.

1.	4.5	×	7	=
2.	3.8	×	6	=
3.	1.29	×	3	=
4.	0.07	×	9	=
5.	6.4	×	8	=
6.	5.13	×	5	=
7.	9.78	×	4	=
8.	7.03	×	8	=
9.	6.25	×	7	=
10.	4.48	×	9	=

Colour in your score

Test 12

Test 13 **Number problems (1)**

Read the questions carefully and work out the calculations you need.

Write the answers to these questions.

1. How much heavier is 5.19kg than 3.73kg?

2. What is 5.39cm add 7.06cm?

3. A jug holds 500ml of drink. If 87.5ml is poured out, how much drink is left in the bottle?

4. Kate has £86.42. She has £27.29 more than Hannah. How much money does Hannah have?

5. If you bought 2 items for £66.74 and £92.85, how much change would you get from £200?

6. A piece of wood was cut into 8 equal lengths, each measuring 9.6cm. How long was the piece of wood before it was cut?

7. What is the total cost of £14.57, £26.92 and £18.65?

8. What is the difference in weight between 400g and 133.5g?

9. A car travels 42.7km on Monday, 39.6km on Tuesday, 54.9km on Wednesday, 27.5km on Thursday and 48.3km on Friday. What is the total distance travelled?

10. The same car travelled 127.8km on Saturday and 96.5km on Sunday. How much further did the car travel in total at the weekend than during the week?

Colour in your score

Test 13

Test 14 Fractions and quantities

To find $\frac{2}{3}$ of £24:
- find $\frac{1}{3}$ of £24 = £8
- then $\frac{2}{3}$ is £8 x 2 = £16

$\frac{2}{3}$ of £24 is £16

Write the answers to each of these problems.

1. What is three quarters of 80?

2. What fraction of 1 hour is 40 minutes?

3. $\frac{4}{5}$ of 65cm =

4. Find $\frac{7}{8}$ of 400g.

5. What fraction of 2m is 60cm?

6. What is $\frac{2}{5}$ of 700km?

7. Find $\frac{6}{7}$ of 56.

8. $\frac{3}{100}$ of 600ml =

9. What is $\frac{5}{6}$ of 360?

10. What fraction of £12 is 50p?

Colour in your score

Test 14

Test 15 Coordinates

Axes are used to plot **coordinates** on **graphs**.

Plot these positions on the graph.

1. Position A is at (2, 6).

2. Position B is at (-1, 7).

3. Position C is at (5, 6).

4. Position D is at (-2, -7).

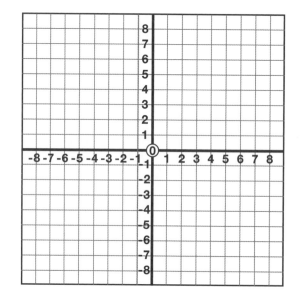

Draw these triangles.

5. Triangle K
   (4, 4) (4, -3) (2, -3)

6. Triangle L
   (-3, 5) (-6, 2) (-1, 1)

7. Triangle M
   (-3, -1) (-6, -4) (-3, -6)

Plot these positions on the graph.

8. Plot the following coordinates: (-4, 6) (0, 3) (-4, 1) (-6, 4). Join them in order.

9. Draw a reflection of the shape.

10. Write the coordinates of this shape.

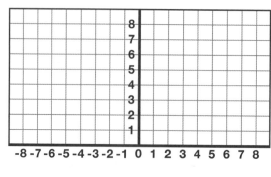

(_ , _) (_ , _) (_ , _) (_ , _)

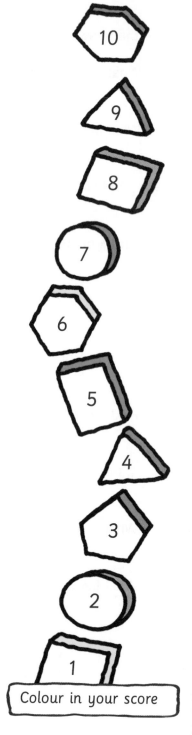

Colour in your score

Test 16 Data handling

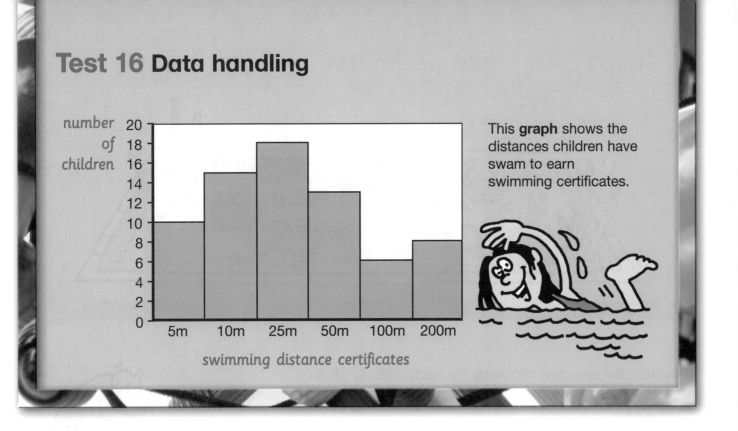

number of children (y-axis: 0, 2, 4, 6, 8, 10, 12, 14, 16, 18, 20)

swimming distance certificates (x-axis: 5m, 10m, 25m, 50m, 100m, 200m)

This **graph** shows the distances children have swam to earn swimming certificates.

Write the answers.

1. How many children got 100m certificates?

2. How many children got 10m certificates?

3. How many children can swim further than 50m?

4. How many more children got 25m certificates than 5m?

5. Which distance had 13 certificates?

6. Which distance had 2 more certificates than the 100m distance?

7. What distance did the least number of children achieve?

8. How many children received certificates?

9. What was the total distance covered by children who achieved 5m certificates?

10. What was the total distance covered by children who achieved 50m certificates?

10
9
8
7
6
5
4
3
2
1

Colour in your score

Test 16

Test 17 Area and perimeter

The **area** of rectangles = length × width.

The **perimeter** is the distance all the way round.

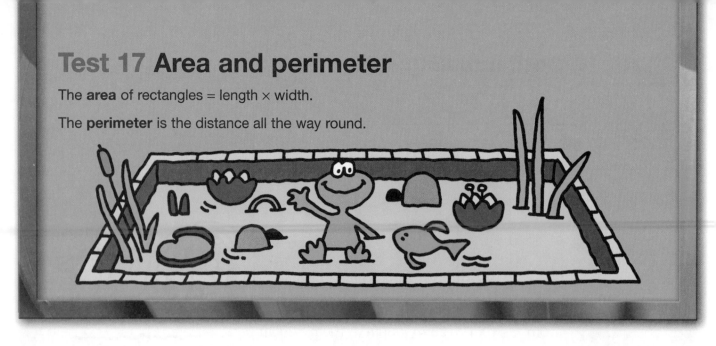

Calculate the area and perimeter for each of these shapes.

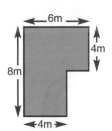

1. area = ☐ m²

2. perimeter = ☐ m

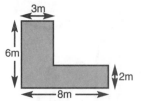

3. area = ☐ m²

4. perimeter = ☐ m

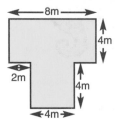

5. area = ☐ m²

6. perimeter = ☐ m

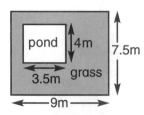

7. What is the area of the pond? ☐ m²

8. What is the perimeter of the pond? ☐ m

9. What is the area of the whole garden? ☐ m²

10. What is the area of the grass? ☐ m²

Colour in your score

Test 17

Test 18 Addition and subtraction (2)

Estimate the answer to the nearest whole number first and then calculate.

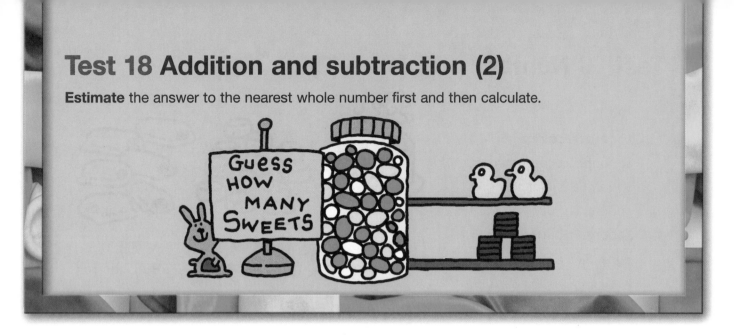

Write the approximate answer to the nearest whole number.
Write the actual answers.

| 8.9 + 6.2 | 1. Approx : | |
| | 2. Actual : | |

| 4.3 + 9.6 | 3. Approx : | |
| | 4. Actual : | |

| 7.7 + 8.8 | 5. Approx : | |
| | 6. Actual : | |

| 4.2 + 9.8 | 7. Approx : | |
| | 8. Actual : | |

| 3.9 + 7.5 | 9. Approx : | |
| | 10. Actual : | |

Colour in your score

Test 18

Test 19 Number problems (2)

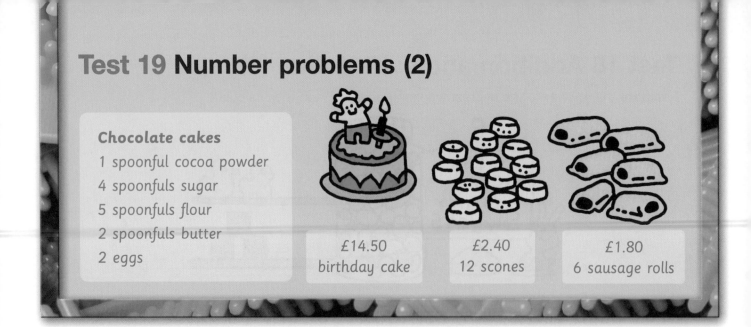

Chocolate cakes

1 spoonful cocoa powder
4 spoonfuls sugar
5 spoonfuls flour
2 spoonfuls butter
2 eggs

£14.50
birthday cake

£2.40
12 scones

£1.80
6 sausage rolls

Use the recipe above to answer these problems.

1. If 1 spoonful is 25g and 1 egg is 30g, how much cake mixture will be made using this recipe?

2. How many 45g cakes can be made from this recipe?

3. If 15 spoonfuls of flour are used, how many spoonfuls of butter will be needed?

4. If 16 spoonfuls of sugar are used, how many eggs will be needed?

5. The cakes take 25 minutes to cook. If they are put in the oven at 5.48 pm, what time will they be ready?

Use the prices above to answer these problems.

6. How much more does 1 sausage roll cost than 1 scone?

7. What change would you have from £20 if you bought a birthday cake, a pack of scones and a pack of sausage rolls?

8. The packs of scones are on offer, 'Buy 2 get 1 free'. How much would it cost for 9 packs?

9. Birthday cakes are reduced by 20%. What is the new price?

10. There are 36 guests at a birthday party. What is the total cost for 1 birthday cake and enough packs of sausage rolls and scones for the guests to have 1 of each?

Colour in your score

Test 19

Test 20 Properties of numbers

Numbers all have different properties.

9

9 is a square number (3^2)
9 is a multiple of 3 (3×3)
9 is an odd number

Which of these numbers is:

| 63 | 50 | 81 | 23 |

1. a square number?

2. a multiple of 7?

3. an even number?

4. a prime number?

Which of these numbers is:

| 24 | 17 | 27 | 15 | 64 | 14 |

5. a factor of 60?

6. a multiple of 6?

7. a factor of 56?

8. a multiple of 9?

9. a square number and a multiple of 8?

10. an odd number and a factor of 34?

Colour in your score

Test 20

Test 21 Decimals (1)

The **decimal point** separates **units** from **tenths**.

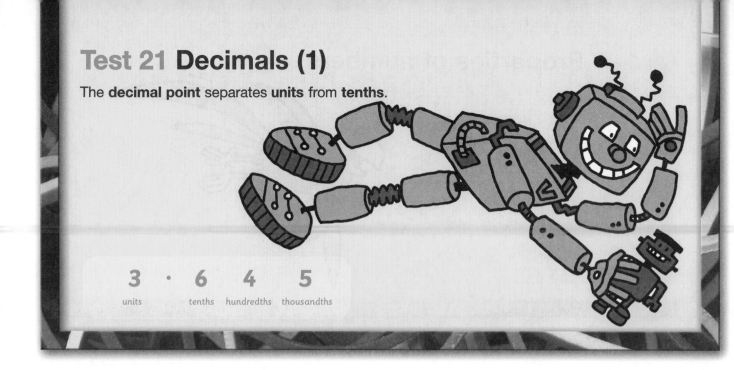

3	·	6	4	5
units		tenths	hundredths	thousandths

Write the value of the bold digit.

1. 42.13**5** ⟹

2. 8.0**9** ⟹

3. 12.7**2**6 ⟹

4. 390.**5**48 ⟹

5. 41.60**7** ⟹

6. 7.9**5** ⟹

Make a decimal number as near as possible to 5.

(There must be one number in front of the decimal point.)

7. (• 7 0 5 2) ⟹

8. (9 3 1 • 4) ⟹

9. (4 • 5 9 0) ⟹

10. (2 6 7 1 •) ⟹

10
9
8
7
6
5
4
3
2
1

Colour in your score

Test 22 Multiplication

It is sometimes better to use a **written method** for multiplying large numbers.

Calculate the answer for each of these.

1.
```
   2 5 3
 ×  1 7
```

6.
```
   1 6 7
 ×  2 1
```

2.
```
   4 9 6
 ×  3 2
```

7.
```
   2 8 5
 ×  2 5
```

3.
```
   8 0 4
 ×  2 4
```

8.
```
   3 1 9
 ×  4 7
```

4.
```
   1 1 5
 ×  4 6
```

9.
```
   7 0 4
 ×  3 5
```

5.
```
   3 2 9
 ×  1 8
```

10.
```
   5 6 8
 ×  3 3
```

Colour in your score

Test 23 Division

Use a **written method** to work out division using large numbers.

Answer these.

1. 14) 7 8 4

2. 27) 9 4 5

3. 35) 6 3 0

4. 18) 4 3 2

5. 33) 9 5 7

6. 19) 5 8 9

7. 26) 4 4 2

8. 32) 4 1 6

9. 21) 8 8 2

10. 16) 6 2 4

Colour in your score

Test 23

Test 24 Decimals (2)

To **order decimals**, line them up with the decimal point aligned.

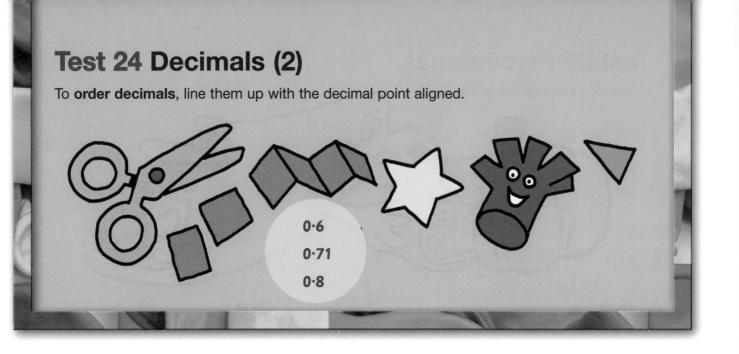

0·6
0·71
0·8

Write these numbers in order, starting with the smallest.

1. 0·9 0·09 0·89 ▷ ☐ ☐ ☐

2. 0·32 0·23 0·03 ▷ ☐ ☐ ☐

3. 0·04 0·6 0·464 ▷ ☐ ☐ ☐

4. 0·517 0·52 0·702 ▷ ☐ ☐ ☐

Write the decimal number these arrows point to.

5. ☐   6. ☐   7. ☐

0   0.01

Use these 4 cards to make:

| 2 | 7 | 4 | • |

8. a number as close as possible to 5.   ☐

9. a number as close as possible to 3.   ☐

10. a number as close as possible to 4.   ☐

Colour in your score

Test 24

Test 25 Percentages

% shows a **fraction** out of **100**.

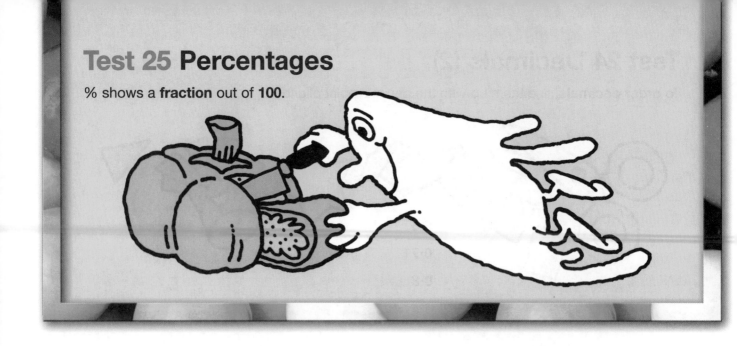

Write these fractions as percentages.

1. $\frac{3}{10}$ =

2. $\frac{7}{20}$ =

3. $\frac{4}{25}$ =

4. $\frac{2}{5}$ =

Write these amounts.

5. 30% of 200ml =

6. 10% of 400kg =

7. 80% of 100cm =

8. 5% of 80g =

9. 25% of 400m =

10. 15% of 60l =

10
9
8
7
6
5
4
3
2
1

Colour in your score

Test 25

Test 26 Data

This graph shows the number of bananas and apples sold in the school tuck shop over a term.

_____ apples

.... bananas

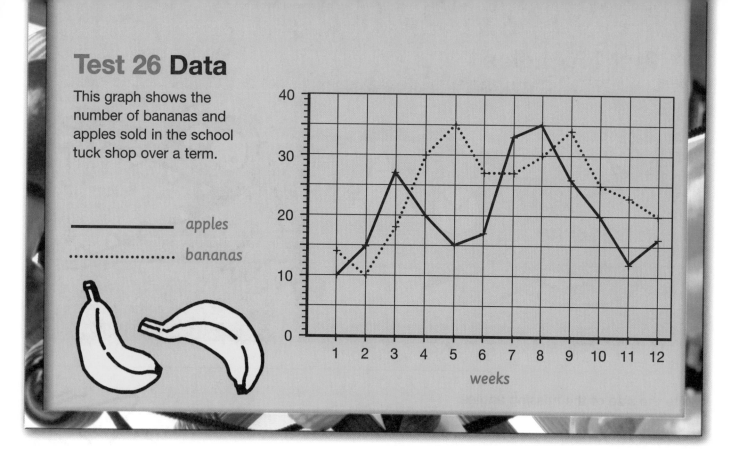

weeks

Answer the following questions.

1. How many bananas were sold in week 8?

2. In which week were most apples sold?

3. In which week were 23 bananas sold?

4. How many more bananas were sold in week 5 than apples?

5. How many apples were sold in week 12?

6. In which week were the fewest apples sold?

7. What is the difference between the numbers of bananas sold in week 4 and week 5?

8. Which weeks were more apples sold than bananas?

9. In which week was the most fruit (bananas and apples) sold?

10. How many apples were sold in total this term?

Colour in your score

Test 26

Test 27 Angles

It is important to remember the rules about **angles**.

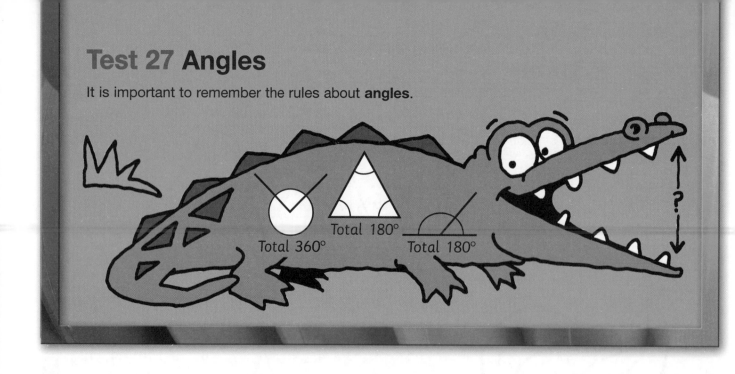

Total 360°

Total 180°

Total 180°

Write the size of the missing angles.

1. 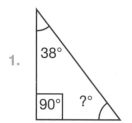 38° 90° ?° ☐

2. ?° 40° 56° ☐

3. ?° 74° 59° ☐

4. 35° ?° ☐

5. ?° 136° ☐

6. ?° 78° ☐

7. ?° 297° ☐

8. ?° 25° 49° ☐

9. 208° 78° ?° ☐

10. 63° ?° 87° 75° ☐

10
9
8
7
6
5
4
3
2
1

Colour in your score

Test 27

Test 28 Time

am ➡ before midday

pm ➡ after midday

The 24-hour clock uses 4 digits.

Write these times using am and pm.

1. 15.37 ➡ [ ]

2. 09.10 ➡ [ ]

3. 13.24 ➡ [ ]

4. 10.15 ➡ [ ]

Write these times using the 24-hour clock.

5. 6.22 am ➡ [.]

6. 9.40 pm ➡ [.]

7. 11.05 pm ➡ [.]

8. 10.48 am ➡ [.]

Write these times 25 minutes earlier.

9. 16.13
⬇
[ ]

10.  ➡ [ ]

Colour in your score

Test 28

When adding and subtracting **decimal numbers**, make sure the decimal points all line up.

Answer these.

1.
```
    2 5 . 6 2
      9 . 7 0
 + 4 3 1 . 0 8
 _____
```

3.
```
   1 3 2 . 7 5
 -  4 4 . 9 0
 _____
```

2.
```
     6 0 . 2 4
 + 3 9 8 . 9 7
 _____
```

4.
```
   2 5 1 . 1 0
 -  1 7 . 3 6
 _____
```

Use a written method to answer these.

5. 24.5 + 138.74 + 6.09 =

6. 251.92 – 64.83 =

7. 48.66 + 193.78 =

8. 102.23 – 15.97 =

9. 684.7 + 35.62 =

10. 127.5 – 46.88 =

Colour in your score

Test 29

Test 30 Equations

Equations have **symbols** or **letters** instead of numbers.

Work out the value of each letter.

1. $7 + x = 15$

    $x = \boxed{}$

2. $18 - y = 11$

    $y = \boxed{}$

3. $\dfrac{a}{4} = 3$

    $a = \boxed{}$

4. $5b = 30$

    $b = \boxed{}$

5. $12 - 2c = 2$

    $c = \boxed{}$

6. $3x - 9 = 15$

    $x = \boxed{}$

7. $4y + 3 = 11$

    $y = \boxed{}$

8. $7 + 2a = 23$

    $a = \boxed{}$

9. $5x - 10 = 20$

    $x = \boxed{}$

10. $26 - 4y = 14$

    $y = \boxed{}$

Colour in your score

Test 30

ANSWERS

Test 1
1. 1000
2. 421
3. 785
4. 10
5. 16·03
6. 45100
7. 6338
8. 100
9. 0·34
10. 2·01

Test 2
1. 9
2. 8
3. 7
4. 7
5. 9
6. 3
7. 5
8. 6
9. 4
10. 8

Test 3
1. £39.96
2. £31.25
3. £10.64
4. £103.11
5. £20.03
6. 68cm
7. 880ml
8. £2.62
9. 122cm
10. 400g, 800g, 800g

Test 4
1. $\frac{4}{5}$
2. $\frac{2}{3}$
3. $\frac{3}{4}$
4. $\frac{3}{5}$
5. $\frac{5}{6}$
6. $\frac{1}{2}$ $\frac{3}{4}$ $\frac{5}{6}$ $\frac{7}{8}$
7. $\frac{6}{20}$ $\frac{10}{20}$ $\frac{14}{20}$ $\frac{15}{20}$
8. $\frac{4}{18}$ $\frac{3}{6}$ $\frac{12}{18}$ $\frac{5}{6}$
9. $\frac{4}{20}$ $\frac{6}{20}$ $\frac{10}{20}$ $\frac{15}{20}$
10. $\frac{10}{40}$ $\frac{16}{40}$ $\frac{20}{40}$ $\frac{25}{40}$

Test 5
1. 1:2
2. 2:3
3. 1:4
4. 3:4
5. 1:3
6. $\frac{1}{2}$ or $\frac{3}{6}$
7. $\frac{1}{3}$ or $\frac{3}{9}$
8. $\frac{4}{9}$
9. $\frac{3}{4}$ or $\frac{9}{12}$
10. $\frac{2}{3}$ or $\frac{8}{12}$

Test 6
1. 1, 2, 2, 2, 2, 3, 3, 4, 4, 5, 5
2. 3
3. 3
4. 2
5. 4kg
6. 2kg
7. 4kg
8. 30
9. 27
10. 29

Test 7
1. E
2. rectangle
3. C
4. kite
5. D
6. trapezium
7. quadrilaterals
8. square
9.
10.

Test 8
(answers are approximate)
1. 9 litres
2. 4 litres
3. 2 pints
4. 5 gallons
5. 3·5 pints
6. 2·25 litres
7. 3 gallons
8. 1 litre
9. 8 pints
10. 13·5 litres

Test 9
1. 147
2. 29
3. 364
4. 1700
5. 382
6. 1410
7. 395
8. 70
9. 4520
10. 7600

Test 10
1. -13, -21
2. 51, 63
3. 17, 19.5
4. 16, 22
5. 4, 2
6. -9, -13
7. 1·75, 2
8. 25, 31
9. 32, 2
10. 7, 17

Test 11
1. 35600
2. 8000
3. 81000
4. 2370
5. 178000
6. 900600
7. 40000
8. 11900
9. 7650
10. 22000

Test 12
1. 31·5
2. 22·8
3. 3·87
4. 0·63
5. 51·2
6. 25·65
7. 39·12
8. 56·24
9. 43·75
10. 40·32

Test 13
1. 1·46kg
2. 12·45cm
3. 412·5ml
4. £59.13
5. £40.41
6. 76.8cm
7. £60.14
8. 266.5g
9. 213km
10. 11.3km

Test 14
1. 60
2. $\frac{2}{3}$ or $\frac{40}{60}$
3. 52cm
4. 350g
5. $\frac{3}{10}$ or $\frac{60}{200}$
6. 280km
7. 48
8. 18ml
9. 300
10. $\frac{1}{24}$

Test 15

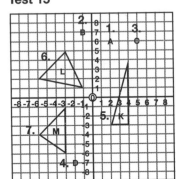

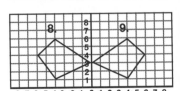

10. (4,6) (0,3) (4,1) (6,4)